£6.45

As you can see, me's wet myself laughing cos me's just had a sneaky peek at 'is brilliant Beano Annual! My bruvver Dennis gets to visit annuver planet inside a giant doggie (s'not fair, me should've got to go too!) 'Em Bash Street Kids is REALLY super and yous is sure to enjoy Minnie the Minx in her cool Panto (oh, yes, you are!) Even 'at silly Colonel man made me laugh wif his funny HEE-HEE! story 'at mum read to me. Dere's Ivy an Les Pretent-HO-HO! and 'at crafty Roger the Dodger an'-HO-HO-HOO! <u>DAD! NEED ME'S NAPPY CHANGED!</u>

... DOWNSTAIRS IS THE TARGET RANGE AND SKATE RAMP, FIRST FLOOR IS THE LAB FOR STINK BOMB MAKING AND UP TOP IS THE LOOKOUT POST.

BLOOPRINT

B-BUT WHERE DID YOU GET ALL THIS?

I WANT MY TREE HOUSE BACK!

THAT'S OUR CRICKET PAVILION.

LOO AND BEHOLD! THERE'S OUR LOO.

OH, DEAR! THERE'S MY ANSWER.

HOMEWRECKERS!!!

AAIEE!

RRRIPP! TEAR!

ZOOM!

WELL, AT LEAST I'VE GOT A KIND OF SHED LEFT ...

... PITY I'M IN THE DOGHOUSE THOUGH.

REPAIRS

COMPLAINTS

BILL

FIDO

the TERRIBLE TWOS!

BALL BOY — LITTLE BO PEEP
Little Ball Boy has lost his ball
And doesn't know where to find it.
Leave him alone, he's playing at home
His dad's hid the ball right behind him!

ROGER THE DODGER — HEY DIDDLE HEY DIDDLE
Hey diddle diddle,
Young Roger loves fiddles.
He's dumped his tea with his spoon.
His little cat laughed to see this dodge
But got covered himself . . . laughed too soon!

THERE ARE STATUES GOING UP IN TOWN OF 'FAMOUS PEOPLE' AND . . .

MAYOR OF BASH ST.

AND YOU WANT ONE OF ME — A NOBLE LEADER!

A LEADER?

CHUCKLE!

Just then —

TING . . .

A . . . LING

. . . DONG!

SLURP!

MISTER MAYOR! YOU'LL WANT TO PUT UP A STATUE OF ME, NO DOUBT!

ZOOM

SLURP!

CRUNCH!

PEOPLE HAVE STOOD IN LINE FOR MY FOOD!

NO! A STATUE OF THE FAMOUS 'BASH STREET KIDS'!

HUMPH!

YES!

BUT WE ONLY HAVE ENOUGH SPACE FOR ONE KID! SO, YOU DECIDE WHO! 'BYEE!

AW!

WE'LL LET TEACHER PICK A NAME OUT OF MY HAT!

A FAIR WAY TO DO IT!

OKAY!

THUD!

BIFF!

TUG

WAIT! HOLD IT! THIS IS DAFT! WE'RE ALL GOOD MATES! WE SHOULDN'T BE FIGHTING!

SWISH

GROO!

GROAN!

GROO!

HO-HO! NOT QUITE! IN LINE **AFTER EATING** YOUR FOOD! CHUCKLE!

HUH!

DANNY!

WELL, THANKS!

SUSPICIOUS

But —

DANNY!

DANNY!

GRRR! CHEAT!

I KNOW! LET'S HAVE A BIG PUNCH-UP! THE LAST ONE STANDING WINS!

YES! YOU'RE ON!

SWISH

SWISH

I HAVE ANOTHER IDEA!

← PALS NOW

Much later —

IT GIVES ME GREAT PLEASURE TO UNVEIL THE STATUE OF A FAMOUS PERSON . . .

GNASHER AND GNIPPER

WHEW! I'M HOT!

WE'LL HAVE TO FIND A WAY TO COOL OFF! GASP!

Then —

THIS MAN'S A KEEN GARDENER . . .

. . . I KNEW HE WOULDN'T LET HIS PLANTS WILT! AAAGII!

WHIRR!

WHIRR!

SPLISH!

SPLOSH!

GRRREAT!

But —

WATCH OUT — I MIX 'FAST GROW' IN WITH THE WATER TO HELP THEM SPROUT!

Suddenly, their coats grow —

HA-HA! IT MAKES ANYTHING GROW!

GNEEK!

GROW! GROW!

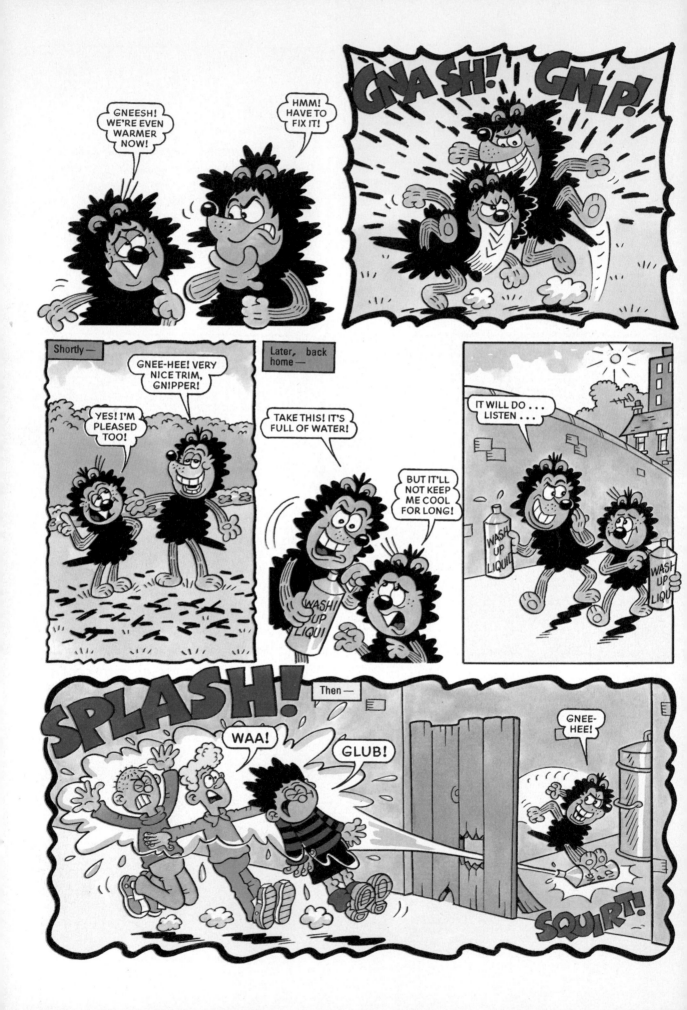

THE COLONEL'S JOURNALS
THE GREAT ANTARCTIC BAGPIPE HUNT
PART 1

Chapter One — Poultry Plague Poses Problems And Panics Parliament

1 It was the year when the dreaded chicken plague struck the country and left the government with egg on their faces. I was summoned to the Houses of Parliament but was held up by a constant stream of chickens who kept crossing the road. When we finally got there, I tipped the taxi driver generously into a dustbin and hurried in.

I rushed to the office of the Minister for Hysteria, where I fell into a heap.

"Why don't you watch where you're goin', Chief?" grumbled the heap, who I now saw was a knock-kneed Cockney with an oversized cap and an undersized body. It was Shambles, my left-handed right hand man.

3 What the Minister had been telling me was that an outbreak of chickens was only the latest in a long list of disasters for Britain. Who could forget the great infestation of penguins (or the even worse penguin shortage once the antidote had been discovered)? Who would forget the flying elephant plague which had led to panic buying of heavy-duty umbrellas? And who could remember the great amnesia epidemic?

5 I wasn't going to take this lying down and, as soon as I'd gotten up off the floor, I declared, "Don't worry, sir. I don't know the meaning of defeat!" This was no lie, as my dictionary only went up as far as "BUNGALOW".

"You don't mean," he asked, "that you've found a cure for chickens?"

"Exactly, sir," I replied. "I don't mean I've found a cure for chickens. What I do mean is that I've a plan to save the nation!"

Shambles and I raced back (I won) to our top secret, ultra security, highly classified headquarters at Number 23B Scrodgers Lane, Beanotown, ZZQ 23 (Top floor, above the chip shop).

"Our mission is so top secret I can't even tell myself about it," I said. "It'll involve travel and you'd best prepare the anti-measles pills in case we're spotted."

All right, you horrible little readers, sit up straight there and pay attention! And stop slouching. Now, then, it's time for some discipline in this book. I was going through my old military records ("Brigadier Terrence Mongoose Sings Ricky Martin", "The R.A.F. Play The Eagles Greatest Hits" and "The Ministry Of Defence Clog Dancing Album"), when I found my journals. So smarten yourself up and prepare for a stirring tale of bagpipes and bravery.

2 I took a seat (but left the coatstand so the woodworm wouldn't go hungry). The Minister, the Right Honourable Gervaise Gibberancringe, was far too panicked to explain why I'd been called for, but I rapidly realised that his knees were knocking in Morse Code. I listened in horror as his knees spelled out disaster.

"Mince prices set to soar?" I gasped. "Polka dot bowler hats to be worn on every third Tuesday of the month and an inflatable stoat to be made Archbishop of Canterbury? It's unbelievable!"

Shambles pointed out that it was unbelievable because it wasn't true. My faithful sidekick had spotted my slight error in decoding the message.

4 The Minister continued. "Tourists are staying away from this country in droves. If this keeps up, sales of Big Ben tea-towels, miniature red London buses, postcards of Snowdonia and heavy duty "Kiss-Me-Quick" plastic rain hats could end and the country will be forced to close and move to smaller premises. That is, unless we can find someone with the pluck to stand up to these chickens and you were first in the pecking order."

6 "We'll need disguises. Fetch Spy-Kit Number 17a; namely one hand woven kilt, one genuine, hand-woven ginger beard and a house-rained sporran."

"D'you want me t'get us train tickets to Scotland, guv'nor?" he muttered as we clambered into our kilts. His was too big for him but mine was a perfect tartan fit.

"Scotland?" I cried. "Looking like this? No, you tiny, toothless, tartan twit. Our next stop is the South Pole!" And, pointing our legs in the direction of South, we set off on our search for the exotic and elusive Bagpipe Herd of Antarctica!

All right, Readers. At ease! You're all dismissed until later in the book when this gripping tale of international intrigue continues. And don't pick that or it'll never get better!

DENNIS AND BEA IN: I'M IN IT TOO! TYRED OUT!

OH, DEAR! I MUST GET RID OF THIS SPARE TYRE!

OH, YER?

Mi HERO
ATTILLA the HUN

YOU JUST NEED SOME EXERCISE, MUM. COME SLEDGING WITH US.

NO WAY! NO SLEDGING!

WHY'S 'AT?

DO NOT ATTEMPT TO REMOVE THIS CLAMP

'COS I HAD SOME FUN SLEDGING LAST YEAR. AND WALTER DIDN'T!

Last year —

GSOFTY!

I SEE HIM!

JUST ADD A SUPER TIARA TO MY SOFTY SNOWPERSON!

SLAM!

?

WOW! THAT SNOWMAN LOOKS JUST LIKE WALTER! HA-HA!

THAT'S WHY THERE IS NO SLEDGING! I'M GOING TO MY DANCE CLASS. COMING?

DANCE CLASS? NO WAY! NO. TA! NOPE! NEVER! YUK!

YUP! WE IS COMING, MUM!

EH? WHAT?

DON'T WORRY, BIG BRUVVER!

WHAT ARE YOU UP TO, BEA?

And—

GARAGE

LOSE FAT HERE! AND BE A FAT LOSER!

SEE 'AT GARAGE NEXT DOOR?

AN' SEE 'AT TYRE?

I GET IT!

NIGEL PARKINSON.

BLOW IT UP, BEA — HUGE!

FREE AIR

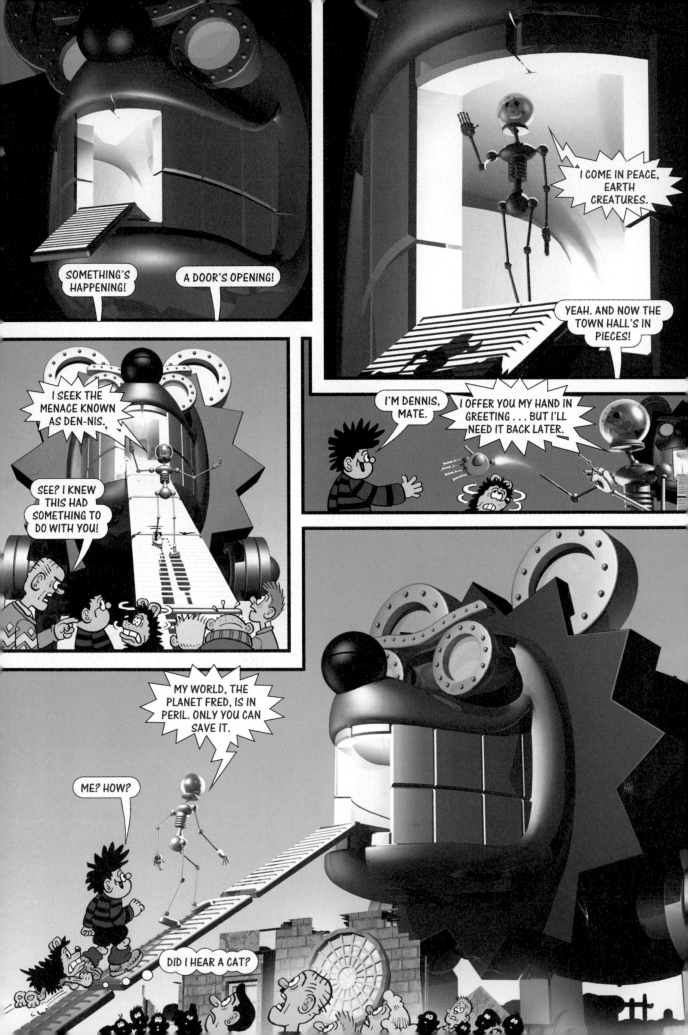

FLIP! BZZT!

WITH THIS!

CLICK!

SPRONG!

WOW! A HYPER-SPACE CATAPULT!

WITH YOUR SKILLS, YOU CAN MAKE THE SHOT THAT'LL PLUG THE HOLE.

And . . .

STRE-E-E-ETCH!

OKAY, THE ASTEROID'S LOADED . . . I'LL JUST AIM FOR THAT UNINHABITED PLANET.

TWOING!

WHEEEE!

FIRE!

WHACK!

CRACK!

ZOOOM!

WAK!

ZIP!

WHOOSH!

ZING!

SMACK!

WHUMP!

ZOOOOM!

WELL POTTED!

AND IT WASN'T JUST POT LUCK!

WHOOSH!

TIME TO TAKE YOU HOME.

OKAY, SPACE BLOKE, BUT JUST DO ME ONE FAVOUR . . .

And . . .

WHY HAVEN'T YOU DONE YOUR HOMEWORK, BOY?

SORRY, SIR. THE DOG ATE IT.

Teecher is a nit

true

our beloved leeder NOT!

THE DOG ATE YOUR HOMEWORK? A LIKELY STORY.

NO, SIR. IT DIDN'T EAT MY HOMEWORK.

MUNCH! CRUNCH!

IT ATE THE SCHOOL!

HOORAY!

NICE DOGGIE!

The End

the TERRIBLE TWOS!

IVY — MARY, MARY QUITE CONTRARY
Ivy, Ivy, quite contrary,
How do your guardians cope?
You give them hell, you shout and yell.
We pity them once you have grown!

BILLY WHIZZ — WEE WILLIE WINKIE
Wee Willy Whizz he runs through the town —
Upstairs downstairs never slows down.
Whizzing past your window, zipping past your door.
Wears out all his baby grows and worn out half the floor!

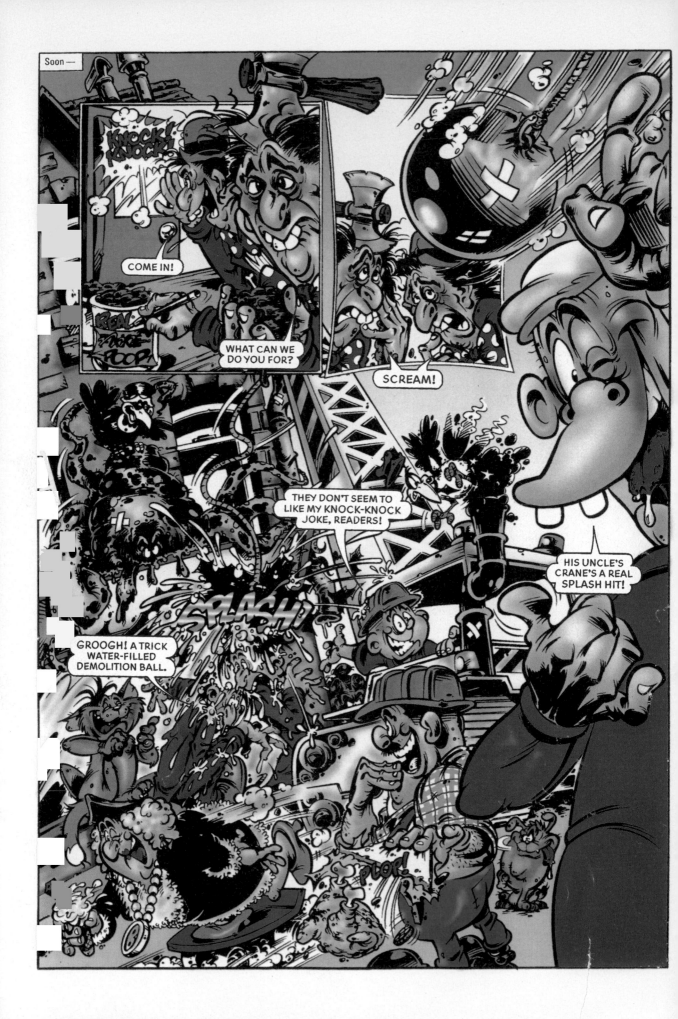

ALL THESE STRANGE THINGS HAPPENING LATELY . . .

THIS OAR DIDN'T BREAK. IT WAS CUT!

THANKS FOR GETTING YOUR MODELS TO HELP, JUMBO. GRANDPA'S GOT LOTS OF MODELS IN THE COTTAGE.

And . . .

THIS IS CAPTAIN BLUEBRISTLE'S PRIVATEER, "THE WOLFHAWK".

SHE WERE A TREASURE SHIP, RUN AGROUND BY WRECKERS NEARLY TWO-HUNDRED YEARS AGO. ALL THAT'S LEFT ARE HER RIBS A-STICKIN' OUT OF THE SAND DOWN ON OUR BEACH.

THE TREASURE WAS NEVER FOUND BUT GRANDPA BELIEVES THAT ON STORMY NIGHTS, THE GHOST OF BLUEBRISTLE STILL HAUNTS THESE SHORES, FOREVER SEARCHING FOR HIS LOST GOLD.

WOW! COOL STORY.

Soon . . .

UH-OH! HERE COMES TROUBLE. IT'S ARCH STANTON, THE PROPERTY DEVELOPER WHO'S BEEN TRYING TO PERSUADE GRANDPA TO SELL OUR COTTAGE.

IS THAT RIGHT? HMM . . .

But . . .

I WAS BORN IN THIS COTTAGE AN', ONE DAY, IT'LL BE KATIE'S!

IF IT STAYS STANDING THAT LONG.

GRANDPA WILL NEVER SELL.

COME NOW, MR MARNER. YOU'RE MAKING A *BIG* MISTAKE.

Next morning . . .

JUMBO! SOMEONE BROKE IN LAST NIGHT AND TOOK THE MODEL OF THE WOLFHAWK. WE FOUND IT LYING SMASHED IN THE RIBS OF THE WRECK.

OH, NO!

GRANDPA THINKS . . . WELL, HE THINKS IT WAS CAPTAIN BLUEBRISTLE'S GHOST!

And . . .

THERE WAS A BLINDING LIGHT AND I SAW HIM! HE SAID HE WOULD BE BACK AND THAT THERE'S WORSE YET TO COME!

I ONLY HEARD THE WIND AND THE WAVES. OLD SAILORS CAN BE VERY SUPERSTITIOUS.

THERE'S ANOTHER STORM COMING TONIGHT. MAYBE WE SHOULD THINK ABOUT STANTON'S OFFER AFTER ALL.

DON'T LET HIM MAKE ANY DECISIONS UNTIL TOMORROW, KATIE. I HAVE A PLAN.

INVOLVING OUR LAUNDRY? *THIS* I'VE GOT TO SEE.

LES PRETEND
THE LITTLE KID WITH THE BIG IMAGINATION

SIGH! IT'S NOT EASY TEACHING TEENAGERS, I CAN TELL YOU.

TINY TOTS NURSERY

MORNING, CLASS 4B! I TRUST YOU'VE ALL DONE YOUR MATHS HOMEWORK.

IGGY-WIGGY — WOOGUMS!

SMACK!

OOF!

GOOGIE-GOO!

SPEAK PROPERLY AND STAND UP WHEN YOUR TEACHER ENTERS THE ROOM.

WE IS STANDIN'!

WE'S ONLY LIKKLE SHORTY-BOTTIES.

YOU'RE LEARNING NORTH AMERICAN HISTORY TODAY SO WATCH THE BOARD WHILE I RUN THROUGH IT.

BAH! MUMSIE'S GAVE ME HOWWIBLE 'NANA AGAIN.

TOSS

AAGH! WHAT STUPID SCHOOLBOY PRANK IS THIS?

HOO-HOO! HIM'S A FUNNY MAN.

SKID!

SMASH!!

YAAROO!

HIM'S RUN 'FROO IT ALRIGHT.

His captain at cricket sent James to the wicket,
He gave the first ball a fine clout.
It flew through the air,
Then total despair —
When all of his team mates were OUT!

BOP! BOP! BOP! BOP! BOP!

"And now on the tee . . ." Alas! Dearie me!
It's James in the 'latest' golf gear.
And then, here's the rub,
Let go of his club —
The end of poor Tiger's career.

TIGER

THUNG!

In one final bid, this brave, stupid kid
Thought tiddlywinks couldn't cause harm.
He tiddled too strong
It flew far and long
And set off a burglar alarm.

BURGLAR ALARM

TRRING!

SMASH

Robbie Rebel!
NOBODY TELLS HIM WHAT TO DO!

NOW, BE A GOOD BOY AND HELP MUM WITH HER SHOPPING . . .

I COULD JUST MAKE MY ESCAPE THROUGH THE WINDOW.

SHOPPING LIST
BREAD
POP
TOMATOES
EGGS
CHEESE
MAYONNAISE
POTATOES
LETTUCE
MUSTARD
P.T.O.

BOW WOW!

. . . OR NO PRESENTS!

SLAM!

JUST . . . ER . . . CHECKING FOR RAIN.

NO FISHING

So . . .

THERE! NICE AND SMART FOR YOUR VISITING RELATIVES.

THERE ARE LIMITS, Y'KNOW . . . BUT I HAVE TO BEHAVE.

I CAN'T LOOK.

GIVE AUNTIE NORENE A BIG KISSIE.

GULP! JUST ONE MORE DAY! ONE MORE DAY! ONE MORE DAY!

BLOIK!

SHAN'T!

WHO SAYS?

THAT'LL SHOW 'EM! THE REBEL IS BACK!

WEIRD BOY.

WHO SAYS?

SNIFF!

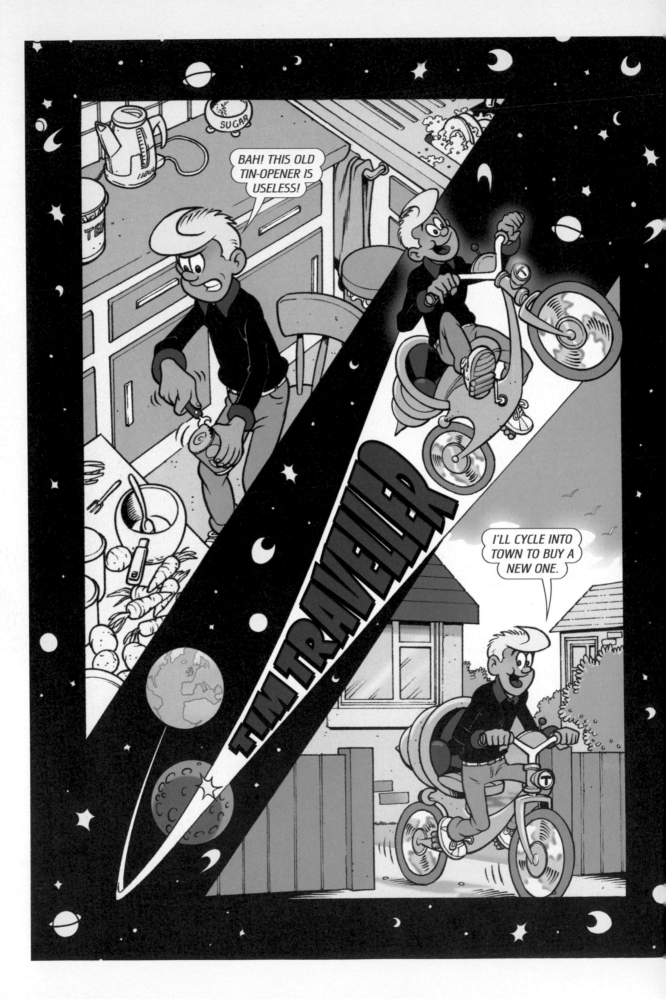

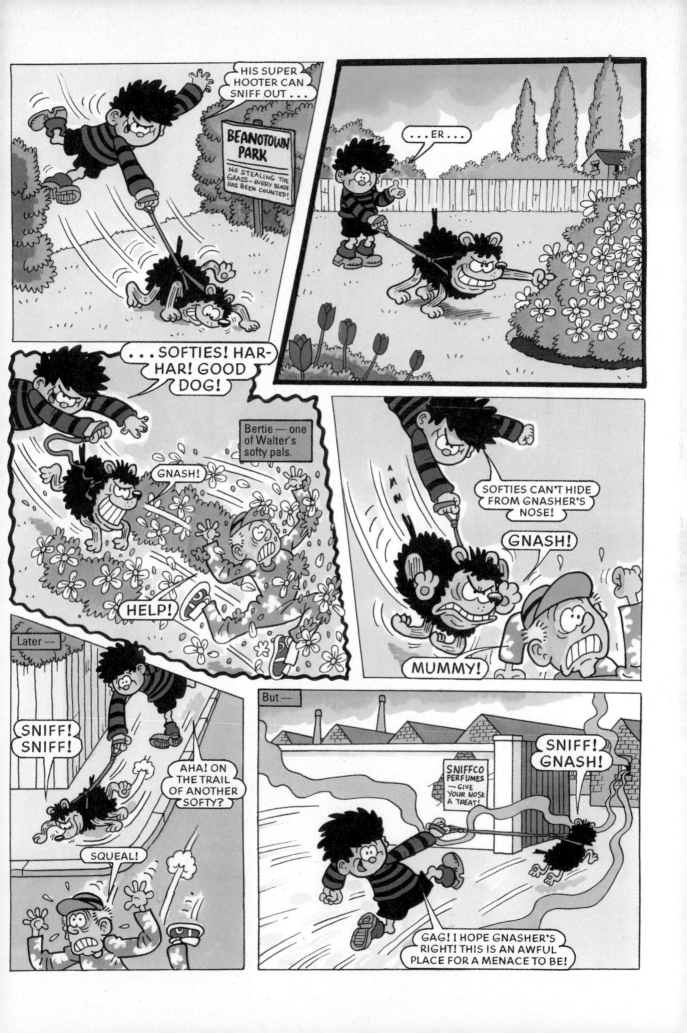

NICE SMELL MAKER

PATENTED PONG PRETTIFIER

SMELLS NICE

LOVELY WHIFF JUICE

PRETTY PONG OF PANSIES

LOVELY FRAGRANCE OF FOREST FLOWERS

HUH! NO-ONE IN HERE, BOY!

GNASH!

SNIFFCO PERFUMES

Suddenly —

AW, NO! FOUND ME!

Spotty — very soft chap.

WELL DONE, GNASHER! NO FOOLING YOU!

WHAT AN AMAZING TALENT MY MENACE HOUND HAS! HAW-HAW-HAW!

YIKES!

GNASH! GNASH!

Next —

GO ON, GNASHER! SNIFF OUT WALTER, PRINCE OF SOFTIES NOW!

SNIFF

SNORF

Soon —

GNASH!

HAND CAR WASH

OPEN

HMM! HIS HOOTER MAY BE OFF TARGET HERE, I THINK!

GNASH! GNASH!

Then —

AHA! GNASHER BLEW WALTER'S COVER! GOOD WORK!

OH, NO!

BLOW

Walter — Prince of Softies.

NOWHERE TO HIDE FOR YOU SOFTIES! HO-HO-HO!

GNASH! HELP! MUMSIE!

Later

WE MUST GET OUR OWN BACK ON THAT HORRID DOGGIE!

LISTEN, CHAPS — HERE'S HOW WE'LL DO IT!

SOFTIES' SECRET WENDY HOUSE

Soon —

Mi HeRo

GENGHIS KAHN

HMM!

BEANOTOWN ZOO

MANURE FOR SALE

TUM...TEE...TUM!

Delia's Deli

IF IT'S PICKLED OR POTTED, WE SELL IT!

STRANGE INEDIBLE NOSH FROM ALL OVER THE WORLD!

TRA...LA...LA!

The BEANOTOWN PLAYERS PRESENT....

It's PANTO TIME!

OH, NO, IT ISN'T!

OH, YES, IT IS!

NOW WHICH PANTOMIME CAN BEANOTOWN THEATRE PUT ON THIS YEAR?

'AT'S IT, GNIPPER PULL BACK A BRANCH . . .

RIGHT, WE NEED A GIRL TO PLAY CINDERELLA.

OH-OH!

NO GIRLS AROUND HERE, MATE.

Deep voice

PAINT

TOUGH LUCK, MINDERELLA — WE KNOW YOU GO TO A DIFFERENT LOO THAN US.

OK — WE NEED PEOPLE TO PLAY BUTTONS, BARON HARD UP, THE FAIRY GODMOTHER AND PRINCE CHARMING.

THE CRIMSON and BLACK PIRATE

A flag fluttered at the top of the ship's mast, just above the crew's undies, which were drying nicely in the breeze.

"Arr, Gnasher!" said Dennis.

"There be a pirate ship we can join and Menace on the High Seas!"

"Gnyip!" agreed Gnasher, although he wondered why the background of the flag was pink instead of black, and why the emblem was a teddy and crossed knitting-needles . . . oh yes, and what was a pirate ship doing in the paddling-pool?

Quickly donning pirate costumes from their dressing-up box. They clambered over the ship's side, where a horrid sight met their eyes. A horde of hideous pirates were sitting on the deck, but that wasn't the horrid thing — the pirates were *knitting!* A cold shiver ran down Dennis' spine (it then jogged along his hip and walked down his thigh).

In the centre of the circle sat a man, dressed in extravagant silken clothes. He was chanting. "Knit one, purl one. Knit one, purl one . . ." He had a rich, curly beard, only it wasn't like normal pirate beards — this one was pink!
"That's the notorious Cap'n Pinkbeard!" whispered Dennis.

"All the toughest pirates were afraid of him. Even Captain Birdseye!"
Dennis strode across the deck towards the pirate crew. "Captain!" he cried.
"Eek!" yelled Pinkbeard, and dived into a nearby water barrel.
"Spoo!" Pinkbeard spouted water from his mouth when he climbed out of the water barrel.
"Wh–what do you want, you nasty boy?"
Dennis puffed out his chest (with the aid of an inflatable ring he wore under his shirt). "*I* wanna be a pirate, and pillage and plunder, and make people walk the plank, and . ."

"Wait, wait," interrupted Pinkbeard. "We don't do that sort of thing. We're *NICE* pirates. We help old ladies cross the Spanish Main and knit nice curtains for the portholes on our ship, 'The Fluffy Poodle'."
"Don't you even have a plank, then?" asked Dennis, who looked as though he'd lost a ten–pound note and found a 'Maths is Fun' video.
Pinkbeard pointed to the side of the ship. "We use it as a place for potted plants now. Pretty, isn't it? I say, you don't crochet, do you? We could do with someone who can crochet!"
Dennis backed away. "Gnasher, this is awful! No wonder all the pirates are scared of them — they're *SOFTY PIRATES!* We've got to stop them before they ruin the seas for all the other pirates!"

"Never!" yelled Dennis, and dropped off the end of the plank. As he fell, he grabbed the very edge of it and called out for his doggy chum: "Now, Gnasher, now!"
Gnasher hurtled along the plank. Pinkbeard turned and looked in horror at the black cannonball-like missile heading directly for him.
"NOOOOOO!" he moaned.

Crash! Gnasher knocked Pinkbeard off the plank, and the softy pirate landed in the paddling pool with a great splash!
"Boo-hoo!" he wailed. "I'm all wet!"
"You were wet before you landed in there, Pinkbeard! Go home to your Mummy and your cuddly pink teddy!"

Dennis climbed back onto the deck of the 'Fluffy Poodle'.
"Come on, Gnasher," he said. "There's something we have to do . . ."
So down came the pink Jolly Roger and another was hoisted in its place. One with a skull and crossbones — a big mistake with Sea Dog Gnasher around!

CALAMITY JAMES
and his pet— ALEXANDER LEMMING!

SHINE THAT SNITCH OF YOUR'S OVER HERE, RUDOLPH. IT'S A LETTER FROM JAMES.

SANTA'S MAIL BAG.

CRIMBO PREZZIES

It's Christmas Eve at the North Pole (and everywhere else, too!)

WoT I doNt wANt for ChRiSSMuS, by JaMeS...

DeeR SaNta, for KriSSMuS this yEeR, pLeeze doN't bRiNg mE... p.t.o. →

A LITTLE SQUELCHY XMAS THINGY.

a DiaRY An' CAlindAR SeT...

BETTER NOT MAKE ANY APPOINTMENTS THIS YEAR.

URTLE! WHEEE!

Y GRAVY CTORY

DIARY		CALENDAR	
FRI	13	FRI	13
FRI	13	FRI	13
FRI	13	FRI	13
FRI	13	FRI	13
FRI	13	FRI	13

JAMES'S FURRY LITTLE LEMMING CHUM ~ ALEXANDER

TIME TO FEED LITTLE BILLY HIS DIN-DINS.

SU-UCK! BURP!

LEMMING JUICE

FISHY NOSH

SKIP!

aN aQUArium

YUM-YUM! FRESH MORON!

NYAARK!

THIS IS JUST LIKE BEING A REAL WILD WEST COWBOY.

TEN GALLON HAT

LEAK.

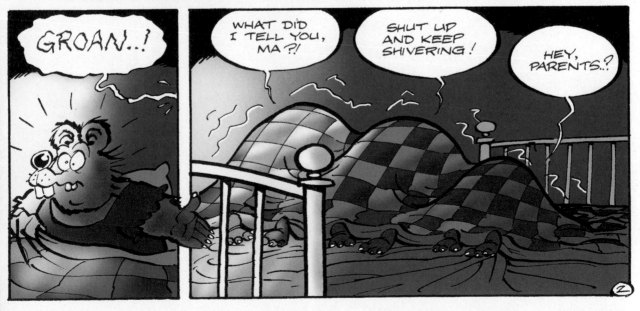

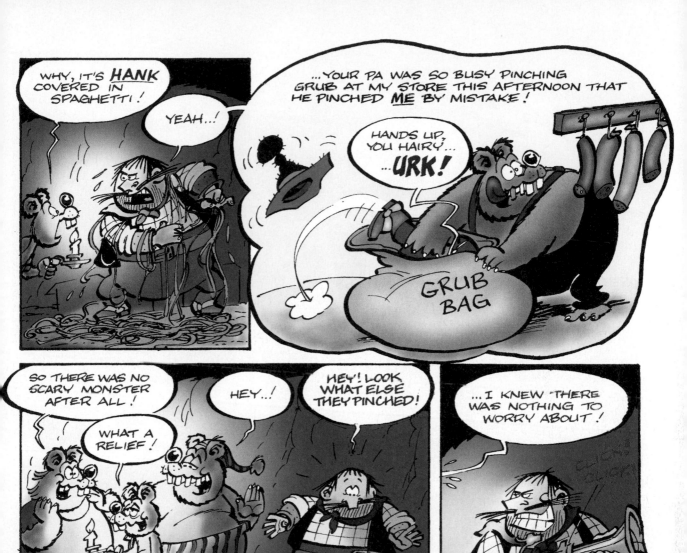

CHRISTMAS CRACKERS

GNASHER AND GNIPPER

Suddenly —

THUMP! GNASHER!

Mum.

GNASHER! DID YOU TOUCH A CAKE LEFT IN THE KITCHEN?

HOME SWEET HOME

CAKE? GNO!

DAZE!

WELL, HOW DO YOU EXPLAIN YOUR TEETH MARKS IN MY CAKE?

EH? BUT I NEVER TOUCHED IT!

HUH! YOU DIDN'T SHARE IT WITH ME!

BUT I NEVER TOOK IT!

Outside —

HMM! WHAT'S THIS?

CAKE CRUMBS!

TROUBLE AHEAD

THIS IS BIG FATHER. YOU CANNOT LEAVE THE TREEHOUSE!

EH? WHERE'D THAT CAMERA COME FROM?

WE HAVE YOU UNDER SURVEILLANCE . . .

GNO WAY! GNOBODY TOUCHES ME OR MY FLEAS!

I NOMINATE DENNIS TO DO IT!

ME, TOO! I NOMINATE DENNIS!

COME ON, NOW, GNASHER, OLD PAL . . .

SPLOSH

PIE-FACE! GET OUT OF GNASHER'S BATH!

BUT IT SMELLS SO GOOD!

WHAT'LL WE GET THEM TO DO NE

HE MADE A REAL DOG'S DINNER OF MY DOG'S DINNER.

. . AND NOBODY GETS T UNTIL YOU COMPLETE THE TASKS WE'VE SET FOR YOU!

FIRST, GIVE GNASHER A FLEA-BATH!

EH?

GNEH?

I'VE BEEN *STOCKING* UP ON BATHTIME TREATS.

BEEFY INSTANT GRAVY MIX! YUM!

EMERGENCY! BATHTIME!

IT'S EARLY THIS YEAR.

NIGEL PARKINSON.

I KNOW! I KNOW!

THIS IS BIG MOTHER. YOUR NECKS ARE FILTHY! TIME FOR A CLEAN . . .

. . . AND TIME FOR A SONG . . . *MAMMA MIA, HERE I GO AGAIN* . . .

THIS ISN'T KARAOKE, WOMAN!

AND IF IT WAS, I'D WOW 'EM WITH MY TOM JONES TURN!

I'LL NEED A CHISEL AND SANDPAPER TO GET THIS GRIME OFF!

AND WASH YOUR SOCKS, YOU 'ORRIBLE LOT! AN ARMY MARCHES ON ITS SOCKS, Y'KNOW!

OUR FATAL FOOT FUMES WILL COVER OUR ACTIONS.

NOT IF WE'RE UNCONSCIOUS, THEY WON'T.

WHAT'S HAPPENED? WHY'S THE PICTURE SO FOGGY?

MUST BE A DASHED WEATHER FORECAST!

IT'S ... IT'S IMPOSSIBLE!

IT'S ... IT'S SPOOKY. WHERE DID THEY VANISH TO?

Here's where ...

SORRY, BUGS!

WARNING, WARREN (WARNING BY WARREN THE BUNNY)

I SHOULD THINK SO, TOO. I'M HOPPING MAD!

TWO CAN PLAY AT THEIR GAME!

DENNIS! LET US OUT!

WHAT? AND SPOIL OUR VIEWING?

THIS IS BIG MENACE! YOUR FIRST TASK IS TO RELOAD ALL PEA-SHOOTERS, PUT FRESH ELASTIC IN CATAPULTS, DO ALL OUR MATHS HOMEWORK . . .

THUD!

CLATTER!

CLANG!

CRASH!

BANG!

THAT'S IT! PUSH THE PIE INTO THE COLONEL'S FACE . . . NOW THE JELLY DOWN SERGEANT SLIPPER'S BOOTS AND A WHOOPEE CUSHION FOR DAD . . .

NOW, THAT'S ENTERTAINMENT!

ME'S DOIN' SOME PLANTIN' NOW.

THERE! NOW IT'S A REAL *POTTY* PLANT.

POTTY

Soon . . .

WIRE NETTING

PLANT POTS

GARDEN TOOLS

WHERE'S BEA GONE? I WISH SHE WOULDN'T JUST *SHOOT* OFF LIKE THAT.

MUM + DAD

COME BACK HERE, DAUGHTER OF MINE!

A LOVELY GREEN BUSHY PLANT

NIGEL PARKINSON

ME GIVE HIM THE RUNAROUND.

PHEW! I'M BUSHED!

SPECIAL OFFER: PAVING £2 CRAZY PAVING £3 TOTALLY BONKERS PAVING £5

LOOK, DEAR. IVY!

EXTRA-STRENGTH FAST-GROWING IVY

OH . . .? *THAT IVY?*

And . . .

AND YOU'LL STAY LIKE THAT TILL YOU TURN OVER A *NEW LEAF.*

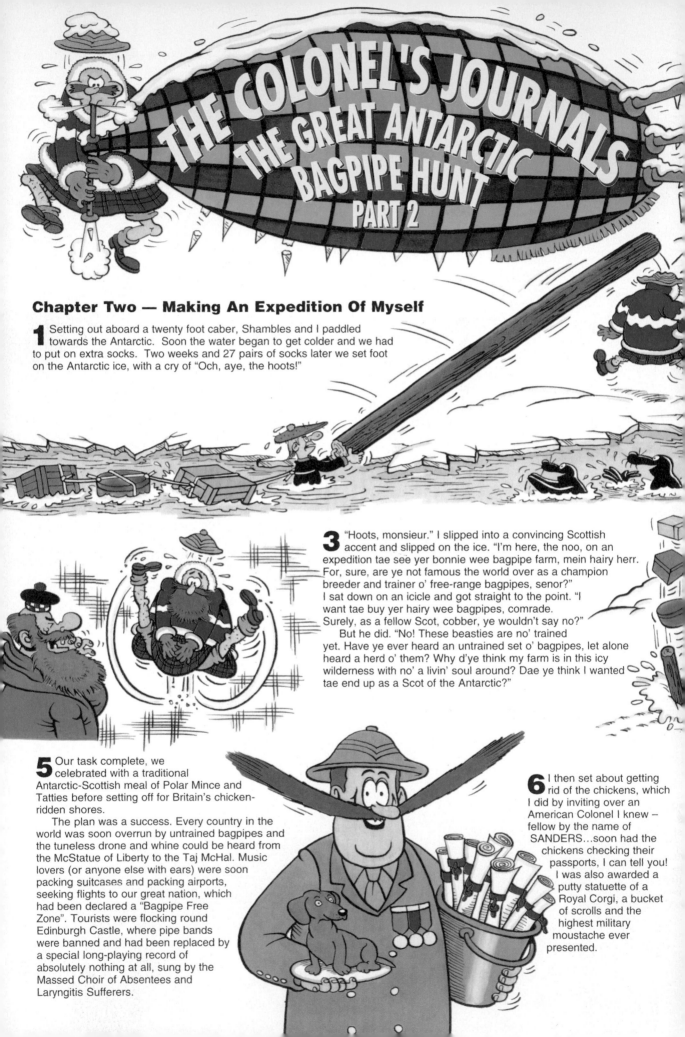

Chapter Two — Making An Expedition Of Myself

1 Setting out aboard a twenty foot caber, Shambles and I paddled towards the Antarctic. Soon the water began to get colder and we had to put on extra socks. Two weeks and 27 pairs of socks later we set foot on the Antarctic ice, with a cry of "Och, aye, the hoots!"

3 "Hoots, monsieur." I slipped into a convincing Scottish accent and slipped on the ice. "I'm here, the noo, on an expedition tae see yer bonnie wee bagpipe farm, mein hairy herr. For, sure, are ye not famous the world over as a champion breeder and trainer o' free-range bagpipes, senor?" I sat down on an icicle and got straight to the point. "I want tae buy yer hairy wee bagpipes, comrade. Surely, as a fellow Scot, cobber, ye wouldn't say no?"
But he did. "No! These beasties are no' trained yet. Have ye ever heard an untrained set o' bagpipes, let alone heard a herd o' them? Why d'ye think my farm is in this icy wilderness with no' a livin' soul around? Dae ye think I wanted tae end up as a Scot of the Antarctic?"

5 Our task complete, we celebrated with a traditional Antarctic-Scottish meal of Polar Mince and Tatties before setting off for Britain's chicken-ridden shores.
The plan was a success. Every country in the world was soon overrun by untrained bagpipes and the tuneless drone and whine could be heard from the McStatue of Liberty to the Taj McHal. Music lovers (or anyone else with ears) were soon packing suitcases and packing airports, seeking flights to our great nation, which had been declared a "Bagpipe Free Zone". Tourists were flocking round Edinburgh Castle, where pipe bands were banned and had been replaced by a special long-playing record of absolutely nothing at all, sung by the Massed Choir of Absentees and Laryngitis Sufferers.

6 I then set about getting rid of the chickens, which I did by inviting over an American Colonel I knew – fellow by the name of SANDERS...soon had the chickens checking their passports, I can tell you! I was also awarded a putty statuette of a Royal Corgi, a bucket of scrolls and the highest military moustache ever presented.

THE STORY SO FAR . . .

Britain has been overrun by chickens. The Colonel has withstood heavy shelling and terrible old yolks to take on a secret mission to save the tourist trade. But why is he dressed as a Scotsman? Why does he expect to find bagpipes at the South Pole? How can bagpipes save the nation? And why does Shambles, his faithful batman, insist on carrying a pineapple in his sporran? Very few of these questions will be answered in this exciting episode.

2 My call was answered by a reeking lump of cold haggis which was hurled at my head by a tall, hairy man in a short, hairy kilt called Hughie. (The man was called Angus MacFumes but his kilt was called Hughie.) I could tell from his knees that MacFumes was a true blue Scotsman but blue knees are to be expected if you're wearing a kilt at the South Pole. "Whit are ye hollerin' aboot, mon?" he growled. "Are ye tryin' tae waken ma bonnie beasties?"

4 "Forget the rotten jokes," I cried. "This is a national emergency, MacFumes.

"We must get tourists back to Britain so we can earn enough to go on holiday away from the frightful place!"

MacFumes drove a hard bargain (the Antarctic's most popular car) but eventually agreed to accept one lead-plated O.B.E. and the secret combination to the Beano Editor's Maximum Security Piggy Bank. Then MacFumes led us to the pastures where frisky young bagpipes grazed and gambolled like a flock of tartan squid.

"Now Shambles," I ordered. "Unstrap four dozen of those wooden crates from round your throat and get these pipes packed and posted."

Soon the entire herd were safely packed away, each with a bag of fresh air to eat on the long journeys ahead of them.

"We're going to send them to every major city outside of Britain," I explained. "Now, unpack that inflatable Post Office so we can buy stamps."

7 It was later, when I was arranging my medals into alphabetical order that I asked, "Shambles. Have you got the scrolls?"

"No, cheeky chops," He replied. "I always walks this way," and he got back to polishing his pineapple. Curiosity was too much for me. I had to ask why my faithful batman carried his odd piece of fruit around with him. What was his terrible secret?

"Simple, chummy. I'm a fruit bat-man!" See? I told you it was terrible.

"DISMISSED!"

WATCH OUT!

Watch out . . . A cat carrier and a microwave oven can be easily mixed up!

Watch out . . . Never do your homework at the breakfast table!

A SPUD IN MY CARRIER? HOPE HE DOESN'T FANCY A BAKED POTATO LATER OR I COULD BE IN THE OVEN.

OOPS! MIXED UP MY JOTTER AND THE TOAST AGAIN!

Watch out . . . Never have a drink of water at Granny's!

SNORE!

YEEOWCH!

Watch out . . . Never play snooker if you keep chickens!

SQUAWK! BEAST!

Watch out . . . Don't store light bulbs near your vegetable rack!

NO, 'ERBERT! THAT ISN'T A LIGHT SNACK!

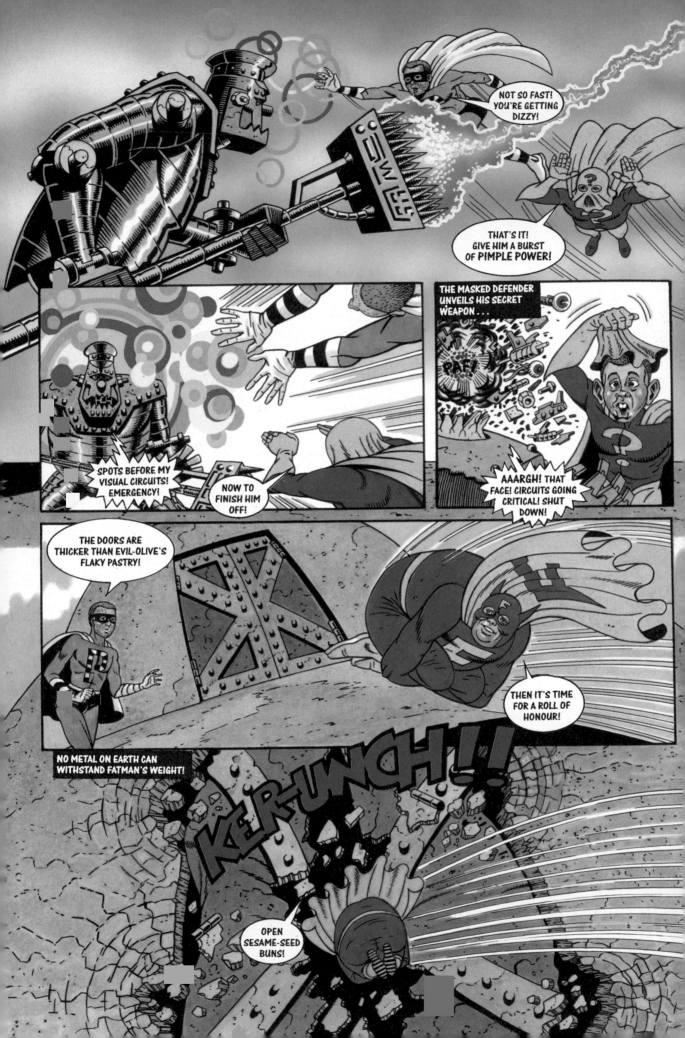

SO, ONCE AGAIN, THE BASH STREET SUPER KIDS HAVE SAVED THE DAY . . . OR HAVE THEY?

DANNY! WHAT IS THE MEANING OF THIS?

ER . . . IT MEANS YOUR LESSON WAS BORING.

RANT! RAVE! READING COMIC STRIPS IN CLASS . . .! MOAN! GRIPE!

HE'S TEARING A STRIP OFF ME.

HUH! SILLY SUPERHEROES! CAN'T SEE WHAT THE KIDS SEE IN . . . HMM . . . FASTER THAN A SPEEDING BULLOCK, EH?

Daydreaming.

IF THERE'S A MATHS PROBLEM TO BE SOLVED OR A HISTORY MYSTERY . . . SEND FOR TEACHERMAN!